J...

SYMPHONY No. 94

G major/G-Dur/Sol majeur
Hob. I:94
"Surprise"
„Paukenschlag-Sinfonie"

Edited by
Harry Newstone

Ernst Eulenburg Ltd

London · Mainz · Madrid · New York · Paris · Prague · Tokyo · Toronto · Zürich

CONTENTS

Ernst Eulenburg Ltd
48 Great Marlborough Street
London W1F 7BB

PREFACE

In the autumn of 1790 Prince Nikolaus Joseph Esterházy, Haydn's employer and patron, died and his son, Prince Paul Anton, succeeded him. Almost at once the great (but considerably expensive) musical establishment which had for nearly 30 years nurtured the composer, and is now chiefly remembered for the glory he brought to it, was dismantled. Although still nominally Kapellmeister, with a yearly pension, Haydn was at last free to travel wherever he wished, something he had not been able to do before. He returned to Vienna relieved of the daily pressures of court duties, but his respite was not to last long. Johann Peter Salomon, the German-born violinist and London impresario, was visiting Cologne when he heard of the death of Prince Nikolaus and lost no time in getting to Vienna determined to procure Haydn for his forthcoming London season. It was not the first time he had invited Haydn to England; now the composer was free to accept, and he did. A contract was exchanged and the two left Vienna in the middle of December and arrived in Dover on New Year's Day 1791.

Haydn stayed in England for a year and a half and returned for a second visit of similar duration in 1794–5. The stimulus he received from the London musical scene, the reception he was accorded there and the high quality of the musicians placed at his disposal inspired him to some of his finest music. The 12 symphonies he wrote for Salomon (six for each visit) are the summation of his orchestral achievement and the ground upon which the music he composed after his return to Vienna – notably the last six masses, *The Creation* and *The Seasons* – was based.

The most popular of the London symphonies are among the most frequently played of Haydn's works, yet for very many years they were (and often still are) performed from texts that had, during the 19th century, become seriously corrupted from the originals. The first modern attempt to present a uniform set of scores based upon authentic sources came with Ernst Praetorius's edition for Eulenburg in the 1930s. For this he consulted the autograph scores of Nos. 98, 99, 101, 102, 103 and 104 but not those of Nos. 94, 95, 96 and 100 (No. 93 has disappeared and the whereabouts of No. 97 was then unknown). One can only speculate on why Praetorius was not able to examine the autograph of No. 94 which was in the then Preußische Staatsbibliothek in Berlin, where he had seen those of Nos. 98, 99, 101, 102 and 104, or Nos. 95 and 96 which were in the British Museum along with No. 103 of which he had received a photocopy. Clearly, detailed knowledge of the whereabouts of Haydn autographs was still very sketchy in the 1930s and Praetorius probably had no way of knowing what we, with the benefit of a further 50 years of Haydn research, can take for granted. Thus Praetorius's edition, while the best available at the time and certainly an important step in the right direction was, not surprisingly, uneven.

The phase of Haydn research that was to result in no less than a renaissance was now well begun. In 1939 the distinguished Danish scholar Jens Peter Larsen published *Die Haydn-Überlieferung* and two years later a facsimile print of *Drei Haydn-Kataloge*, revealing for the first time the immensity of the subject. The postwar years saw the formation in London of the Haydn Orchestra and in Boston of the Haydn Society (both 1949). In 1954, the founder of the Haydn Society, H. C. Robbins Landon, in an article 'The original versions of Haydn's first 'Salomon' symphonies',[1] drew our attention to the extent to which the standard performing editions of these works (mostly Breitkopf & Härtel and Peters) were in many cases 'flagrant falsifications of Haydn's own texts'. For a discussion on how these alterations came about the reader is referred to that article as well as to Landon's *The Symphonies of Joseph Haydn*,[2] and his *Haydn – Chronicle and Works*, Vol. 3 *Haydn in England*.[3]

Since the mid-1950s Henle Verlag, Munich, has issued a number of volumes of Haydn symphonies as part of a Complete Edition of his works for the Haydn Institute of Cologne. Universal Edition, Vienna, issued all the symphonies during the 1960s in an edition by H. C. Robbins Landon.

In 1959, the present writer, with material and advice from Professor Landon, revised and conducted all the London symphonies in a series of BBC broadcasts commemorating the 150th anniversary of the composer's death. The aim was to get as close as possible to Haydn's original intentions not only from the scholar's point of view but from the performer's too.

The texts were accordingly prepared from a number of manuscript sources of primary authenticity and one early printed edition of unusual interest and importance. These same sources, which are listed below with their credentials, have been re-examined for this new edition together with other more recent discoveries.

Editorial Notes

Location and description of sources

I. Autograph scores and authentic
 manuscript copies

We retain, for convenience, the generally accepted numerical order established by Eusebius von Mandyczewski for the Breitkopf & Härtel Collected Edition (begun in 1907 but never completed) although, in the case of the first set of London symphonies, this is not thought to be the order in which they were composed or first performed.

No. 93 Autograph:
 Whereabouts unknown, possibly lost.
 Seen in a Brunswick bookshop in 1870 by the Haydn biographer, Carl Ferdinand Pohl, who noted the date 1791 on it in Haydn's hand.
 Copies:
 1. Copy made in London for Salomon, with corrections in other hands – possibly Haydn's and Salomon's. Acquired by the Royal Philharmonic Society in 1847 from William Ayrton who had inherited all of Salomon's music in 1815. Acquired by the British Library, London, January 1988.[4]
 2. Copy made by Esterházy copyist (Elßler or another with similar handwriting). Esterházy Archives, National Széchényi Library, Budapest.

No. 94 Autograph:
 Movements I, III and IV in the Staatsbibliothek zu Berlin – Preußischer Kulturbesitz, Musikabteilung, lacking last page of Mov. I and the first two pages of the Minuet. The missing page of Mov. I and the whole of Mov. II (in its original version before Haydn added the 'surprise') in the Library of Congress, Washington, D.C.
 Copies:
 1. Salomon's London copy; details as No. 93.
 2. Esterházy copy; details as No. 93. Both with later version of Mov. II (i.e., with 'surprise').

No. 95 Autograph:
 Royal Philharmonic Society collection, British Library, London. Bound together with autograph of No. 96 and copy of No. 98.
 Copies:
 None found – see III below.

No. 96 Autograph:
 Royal Philharmonic Society collection, British Library, London. Bound together with autograph of No. 95 and copy of No. 98.
 Copies:

---

2 London, 1955
3 London, 1976

4 see Arthur Searle, 'Haydn Manuscripts in the British Library', *Early Music*, 5/1982, also *Haydn Yearbook* XIV

None found – see III below.

No. 97 Autograph:
Owned by Mrs Eva Alberman, London (formerly Stefan Zweig collection); acquired by the British Library, London, May 1986.
Copy:
Salomon's London copy; details as No. 93.

No. 98 Autograph:
Formerly in the Preußische Staatsbibliothek, Berlin (from the Schindler Beethoven collection). Four pages missing from Mov. IV. Now in the Jagellonian University Library, Krakow.
Copy:
Salomon's London copy; details as No. 93. Bound together with the autographs of Nos. 95 and 96.

No. 99 Autograph:
Formerly in the Preußische Staatsbibliothek, Berlin. Now in the Jagellonian University Library, Krakow. Photocopy in Hoboken Photogramm Archiv, Vienna.
Copies:
1. Salomon's London copy; details as No. 93.
2. Elßler copy, Esterházy Archives, National Széchényi Library, Budapest.

No. 100 Autograph:
Esterházy Archives, National Széchényi Library, Budapest, lacking Mov. II.
Copy:
Salomon's London copy; details as No. 93.

No. 101 Autograph:
Formerly in the Preußische Staatsbibliothek, Berlin. Now in the Jagellonian University Library, Krakow. Photocopy in Hoboken Photogramm Archiv, Vienna.
Copies:
1. Salomon's London copy; details as No. 93.
2. Elßler copy, Esterházy Archives, National Széchényi Library, Budapest.

No. 102 Autograph:
Staatsbibliothek zu Berlin – Preußischer Kulturbesitz, Musikabteilung, Berlin.
Copy:
Salomon's London copy; details as No. 93.

No. 103 Autograph:
British Library, London: three pages of Minuet in another hand.
Copy:
Salomon's London copy; details as No. 93.

No. 104 Autograph:
Staatsbibliothek zu Berlin – Preußischer Kulturbesitz, Musikabteilung, Berlin.
Copy:
Salomon's London copy; details as No. 93.

It will be seen that, with the exception of No. 93 and the missing slow movement of No. 100, the autograph scores of the London symphonies have survived very nearly intact. The copies made for Salomon in London are a recent (1982) discovery by Alec Hyatt King, and are of great importance.

II. Manuscript orchestral material by Johann Elßler

Orchestral parts copied from the autograph scores by Haydn's own copyist, many with corrections in the composer's hand, are obviously of great value in the establishment of accurate texts of the London symphonies. The most comprehensive collection of the London symphonies is in the Fürstenberg Archives, Donaueschingen, which has them all but No. 100. Some of these parts are on English paper and were evidently used in the original London performances before being taken back to Vienna by Haydn. The Esterházy Archives in Budapest have Elßler parts of Nos. 95, 96, 97, 99, 100, 101 and 103 (the latter lacking the Minuet), and the Oettingen-Wallerstein Archives in Harburg have Nos. 93, 96, 97 and 98.

III. London manuscript scores

In 1795 and 1796 respectively, Haydn presented Salomon with the exclusive rights to both sets of London symphonies, a very proper gesture to the man who had commissioned them and had led the orchestra for the first performances of nine of them (the last three symphonies were presented by the newly-formed 'Opera Concert' at the King's Theatre under the direction of Giovanni Battista Viotti). The tangible aspect of this handsome gift was a complete set of scores – the autographs of Nos. 95 and 96 and copies of the rest, as set out in I above. In November 1791, Haydn sent copy scores of Nos. 95 and 96 to his friend in Vienna, Bernhard von Kees. They evidently arrived safely since von Kees entered the opening bars of both works in his catalogue of Haydn symphonies with the words 'NB von London gekommen', but these scores have not been located.

IV. Printed orchestral material by Robert Birchall, London

There can be no doubt that Salomon also had his own personal set of orchestral parts of all 12 symphonies. He had them engraved, after Haydn's return to Vienna (as the terms of the presentation entitled him to do), with at least one publisher (Monzani & Cimador) and he may also have sold them to others. A year or two after Haydn's death (1809) Salomon entered into an agreement with Robert Birchall (who had earlier published Salomon's arrangements for Piano Trio and for Flute and String Quartet with optional Piano of the London symphonies) for a new issue of the orchestral parts. If Landon is right in supposing that Salomon provided Birchall with his own performing material for this print – possibly the very material he had used under Haydn's direction – it would explain not only the high intelligence and practical nature of the editings, but, more important, the often close relationship between Birchall and the autographs, and the even closer relationship between Birchall and the copy scores that Haydn presented to Salomon.

The Birchall print thus has a high place among the sources upon which this edition is based. With so strong a link – Salomon – between it and Haydn and its readiness as a performing edition, it has a combination of virtues that will be of interest to both scholars and performers. Where the Birchall differs from our other sources (generally because of changes that Haydn made after his return to Vienna that would have been unknown to Salomon) such variants, as well as others of interest, are shown in the Textual Notes below.

Editorial method

Redundant cautionary or parallel accidentals have in some cases been omitted. Haydn's habit of reminding players constantly of such accidentals in continuously modulating passages, even if it means repeating them in the same bar, makes it difficult to follow this aim with complete consistency, and in such cases we have omitted only those which, in modern practice, might confuse rather than clarify.

Missing accidentals, staccato signs, slurs, ties and dynamics etc., have been added without comment only where their absence is the obvious result of the composer's, copyist's or engraver's oversight. Where explanatory comment may be helpful this will be found in the Textual Notes below.

Square brackets and broken ties and slurs indicate editorial additions in the text. The basis for such additions (i.e. parallel or analogous passages) will be clear by the context.

We have retained the indication *Tutti* (used by Haydn to cancel a previous *Solo*, usually in the woodwind) wherever it appears in our sources. Where it is clearly implied by the context but not shown in any of the sources, we have used the modern equivalent – [a 2] where the two parts are in unison.

Since Haydn and Elßler generally wrote a staccato as a quick stroke, it is difficult to determine whether a difference in performance is intended between a stroke and a dot. In general we have used dots except where a sharply accented staccato seems required.

SYMPHONY No. 94

This symphony received its first performance in the Hanover Square Rooms, London, on 23 March at the sixth of Salomon's 1792 series of concerts. Salomon led the orchestra and Haydn directed from the keyboard. It was an enormous success and soon became one of Haydn's most popular symphonies. It remains so today.

The work's additional title, 'Surprise', refers to the loud chord in the second movement, bar 16, a passage that had originally been written without this effect. The name was not the composer's; credit for its invention was later claimed by the London flautist Andrew Ashe who reported that 'my valued friend Haydn thank'd me for giving it such an appropriate Name'.[5] The Symphony is now universally known as the 'Surprise' or, in Germany, by the description 'Mit dem Paukenschlag' (with the kettledrum stroke).

Sources

Autograph score in the Music Collection of the Staatsbibliothek zu Berlin – Preußischer Kulturbesitz, Berlin, and Library of Congress, Washington, D.C. .... AUT
Copy of autograph by Johann Elßler or another Esterházy copyist with similar handwriting, in Esterházy Archives, Budapest .... BUD
Copy of autograph made in London for Salomon .... LON
Manuscript material by Elßler in the Fürstenberg Archives, Donaueschingen .... D/E
Birchall printed edition .... BIR
Occasional reference has also been made to Salomon's Quintet arrangement for checking doubtful notes etc. .... SAL

Harry Newstone

[5] H.C.Robbins Landon, *Haydn – Chronicle and Works* (Vol. 3 *Haydn in England*), (London, 1976), 149

VORWORT

Im Herbst 1790 starb Fürst Nikolaus Joseph Esterházy, Haydns Dienstherr und Gönner; Fürst Paul Anton, sein Sohn, folgte ihm nach. Fast unmittelbar hierauf wurde das bedeutende, allerdings ziemlich kostspielige Musikleben am Hofe eingestellt, das Haydn nahezu dreißig Jahre lang ernährt hatte, und an das man sich heute hauptsächlich des Glanzes wegen erinnert, den es durch den Komponisten erhalten hatte. Obwohl er auch weiterhin den Kapellmeistertitel führen durfte und eine jährliche Pension erhielt, konnte Haydn im Gegensatz zu früher nun schließlich nach Belieben reisen. Er kehrte nach Wien zurück, entlastet vom täglichen Zwang des Dienstes am Hofe, jedoch sollte diese Ruhepause nicht von langer Dauer sein. Als der deutschstämmige Geiger und Londoner Impresario Johann Peter Salomon während eines Aufenthaltes in Köln vom Tod des Fürsten Nikolaus erfuhr, eilte er unverzüglich nach Wien, entschlossen, Haydn für die kommende Saison nach London zu verpflichten. Dies war nicht das erste Mal, dass er Haydn nach England eingeladen hatte; jetzt jedoch war der Komponist in der Lage zuzusagen, und er tat es auch. Ein Vertrag wurde ausgehandelt, und die beiden verließen Wien Mitte Dezember und erreichten Dover am Neujahrstag 1791.

Haydn blieb anderthalb Jahre lang in England und kehrte 1794/95 zu einem zweiten, etwa gleich langen Aufenthalt zurück. Die Anregungen, die er durch das Londoner Musikleben erhielt, die Aufnahme dort und die hohe Qualität der ihm zur Verfügung stehenden Musiker inspirierten ihn zu mehreren seiner bedeutendsten Werke. So bilden die zwölf Sinfonien für Salomon (sechs für jeden Aufenthalt) die Zusammenfassung seiner ganzen Kunst der Orchesterkomposition und die Grundlage für die Werke, die er nach seiner Rückkehr nach Wien schrieb – vor allem die sechs letzten Messen sowie die *Schöpfung* und die *Jahreszeiten*.

Die bekanntesten der Londoner Sinfonien gehören zu den meistgespielten Werken Haydns, jedoch wurden sie viele Jahre lang (vielfach noch bis in die heutige Zeit) aus Notenmaterial aufgeführt, das im 19. Jahrhundert gegenüber dem Originaltext erheblich verfälscht worden war. Den ersten neueren Versuch, aufgrund der authentischen Quellen einen einheitlichen Satz Partituren herauszubringen, stellt die Ausgabe von Ernst Praetorius im Rahmen der Edition Eulenburg in den 1930er Jahren dar. Er zog die Partitur-Autographe von Nr. 98, 99, 101, 102, 103 und 104 heran, nicht aber diejenigen von Nr. 94, 95, 96 und 100 (das Autograph von Nr. 93 ist verschollen, und das von Nr. 97 war damals nicht nachweisbar). Man kann nur Vermutungen darüber anstellen, warum Praetorius nicht in der Lage war, das Autograph von Nr. 94 zu untersuchen, das in der damaligen Preußischen Staatsbibliothek in Berlin lag, wo er auch die Autographe von Nr. 98, 99, 101, 102 und 104 eingesehen hatte; Nr. 95 und 96 waren ihm im British Museum London zugänglich, zusammen mit dem Autograph von Nr. 103, das ihm als Fotokopie vorlag. Auf jeden Fall war die Kenntnis der Aufbewahrungsorte von Haydn-Autographen in den 1930er Jahren noch sehr lückenhaft, und Praetorius konnte damals wohl kaum wissen, was wir heute, nach weiteren 50 Jahren Haydn-Forschung, als erwiesen betrachten können. So war es nicht verwunderlich, dass die Ausgaben von Praetorius in sich uneinheitlich waren, auch wenn sie zu ihrer Zeit die besten verfügbaren waren und sicherlich einen Schritt in die richtige Richtung unternahmen.

Damit hatte eine Zeit intensiver Haydn-Forschung begonnen, die eine regelrechte Renaissance auslöste. 1939 veröffentlichte der bedeutende dänische Musikwissenschaftler Jens Peter Larsen sein Buch *Die Haydn-Überlieferung* und zwei Jahre später als Faksimile *Drei Haydn-Kataloge*; damit wies er erstmals auf die nahezu unüberschaubaren Dimensionen dieses Forschungsbereichs hin. In den Nachkriegsjahren folgten die Gründung des Haydn-Orchesters London und in Boston die der Haydn-Gesellschaft (beide 1949). 1954 machte H. C. Robbins Landon, Begründer der Haydn-Gesellschaft, in einem Aufsatz „The original versions of Haydn's first 'Salomon' symphonies"[1] auf das Ausmaß aufmerksam, in dem das verfügbare Aufführungsmaterial dieser Werke (hauptsächlich von Breitkopf & Härtel und Peters) in vielen Fällen durch „offenkundige Verfälschung von Haydns eigenem Notentext" entstellt war. Bezüglich einer eingehenden Darstellung, wie es zu diesen Abweichungen kam, sei hier auf den zitierten Aufsatz sowie auf Landons Arbeiten *The Symphonies of Joseph Haydn*[2] und *Haydn – Chronicle and Works* (Bd. 3: *Haydn in England*)[3] hingewiesen.

Seit Mitte der 1950er Jahre hat der Henle-Verlag München im Rahmen einer Gesamtausgabe der Werke Haydns durch das Haydn-Institut Köln mehrere Bände mit Sinfonien veröffentlicht. Bei der Universal Edition Wien erschienen alle Sinfonien in den 1960er Jahren in einer Ausgabe von H. C. Robbins Landon.

1959 revidierte der Herausgeber der hier vorliegenden Ausgabe anlässlich einer Sendereihe der BBC zum 150. Todestage des Komponisten, in der er selbst alle Londoner Sinfonien Haydns dirigierte, die Partituren, wofür ihm Robbins Landon eigenes Material und seinen Rat zur Verfügung stellte. Das Ziel war, Haydns eigenen Intentionen nicht nur vom wissenschaftlichen Standpunkt aus, sondern auch aus der Sicht des ausübenden Musikers so nahe wie möglich zu kommen.

Der Notentext wurde aufgrund einer Anzahl handschriftlicher Primärquellen und einer besonders interessanten und wichtigen Druckausgabe erarbeitet. Diese unten verzeichneten und beschriebenen Quellen wurden für die Neuausgabe unter Berücksichtigung anderer neuerer Forschungsergebnisse nochmals untersucht.

Revisionsbericht

Quellen-Fundorte und Quellenbeschreibung

I. Partiturautographe und autorisierte Abschriften

Der Einfachheit halber wird die allgemein übliche Zählung nach der Gesamtausgabe von Eusebius von Mandyczewski bei Breitkopf & Härtel (unvollständig, begonnen 1907) beibehalten, obwohl sie vermutlich für die erste Folge der Londoner Sinfonien weder der Reihenfolge der Entstehung noch der Uraufführungen entspricht.

Nr. 93 Autograph:
Verschollen, möglicherweise verloren. Zuletzt 1870 in einer Braunschweiger Buchhandlung durch den Haydn-Biographen Carl Ferdinand Pohl nachgewiesen, der die Datierung 1791 von Haydns Hand feststellte.
Abschriften:
1. Abschrift aus London, angefertigt für Salomon, mit Korrekturen in anderer Handschrift – vermutlich von Haydn und Salomon. 1847 erworben durch die Royal Philharmonic Society London von William Ayrton, der 1815 von Salomon dessen gesamten Bestand an Noten geerbt hatte. Seit Januar 1988 im Besitz der British Library London[4].
2. Abschrift eines Kopisten am Hofe Esterházy (Elßler, der Haydns Kopist war, oder jemand mit ähnlicher Handschrift): Esterházy-Archiv der Széchényi-National-bibliothek Budapest.

Nr. 94 Autograph:
Satz I, III und IV: Staatsbibliothek zu Berlin – Preußischer Kulturbesitz, Musikabteilung (ohne die letzte Seite von Satz I und die ersten beiden Seiten des Menuetts). Die fehlende Seite von Satz I und der vollständige Satz II (in seiner ursprünglichen Fassung vor der

---

[1] *The Music Review*, Jg. 15/1, 1954.
[2] London 1955.
[3] London 1976.

[4] Vgl. Arthur Searle, „Haydn Manuscripts in the British Library", in: *Early Music*, 5/1982, und *Haydn Jahrbuch XIV*.

Hinzufügung des „Paukenschlags" durch Haydn) befinden sich in der Library of Congress Washington D.C.
Abschriften:
1. Salomons Londoner Abschrift; wie Nr. 93
2. Abschrift Esterházy: wie Nr. 93 (beide mit der späteren Fassung von Satz II, d.h. mit dem „Paukenschlag")

Nr. 95 Autograph:
Royal Philharmonic Society Sammlung, British Library London (zusammengebunden mit dem Autograph von Nr. 96 und der Abschrift von Nr. 98)
Abschriften:
Nicht nachweisbar (vgl. unten Abschnitt III)

Nr. 96 Autograph:
Royal Philharmonic Society Sammlung, British Library London (zusammengebunden mit dem Autograph von Nr. 95 und der Abschrift von Nr. 98)
Abschriften:
Nicht nachweisbar (vgl. unten Abschnitt III)

Nr. 97 Autograph:
Im Mai 1986 aus dem Besitz von Frau Eva Alberman, London, erworben durch die British Library London (vormals Sammlung Stefan Zweig).
Abschrift:
Salomons Londoner Abschrift; wie Nr. 93

Nr. 98 Autograph:
Vormals Preußische Staatsbibliothek Berlin (aus der Beethoven-Sammlung Schindlers). Von Satz IV fehlen vier Seiten. Heute im Besitz der Biblioteka Jagielloæska Krakau.
Abschrift:
Salomons Londoner Abschrift; wie Nr. 93 (zusammengebunden mit den Autographen von Nr. 95 und 96)

Nr. 99 Autograph:
Vormals Preußische Staatsbibliothek Berlin; heute im Besitz der Biblioteka Jagielloæska Krakau. Fotokopien im Photogramm-Archiv Hoboken, Wien
Abschriften:
1. Salomons Londoner Abschrift; wie Nr. 93
2. Abschrift Elßler: Esterházy-Archiv der Széchényi-Nationalbibliothek Budapest

Nr. 100 Autograph:
Esterházy-Archiv der Széchényi-Nationalbibliothek Budapest (ohne Satz II)
Abschrift:
Salomons Londoner Abschrift; wie Nr. 93

Nr. 101 Autograph:
Vormals Preußische Staatsbibliothek Berlin; heute im Besitz der Biblioteka Jagielloæska, Krakau. Fotokopien im Photogramm-Archiv Hoboken, Wien
Abschriften:
1. Salomons Londoner Abschrift; wie Nr. 93
2. Abschrift Elßler: Esterházy-Archiv der Széchényi-Nationalbibliothek Budapest

Nr. 102 Autograph:
Staatsbibliothek zu Berlin – Preußischer Kulturbesitz, Musikabteilung
Abschrift:
Salomons Londoner Abschrift; wie Nr. 93

Nr. 103 Autograph:
British Library London (drei Seiten des Menuetts in fremder Handschrift)
Abschrift:
Salomons Londoner Abschrift; wie Nr. 93

Nr. 104 Autograph:
Staatsbibliothek zu Berlin –Preußischer Kulturbesitz, Musikabteilung
Abschrift:
Salomons Londoner Abschrift; wie Nr. 93

Mit Ausnahme von Nr. 93 und dem fehlenden langsamen Satz von Nr. 100 sind also die autographen Partituren der Londoner Sinfonien nahezu unversehrt erhalten. Die Abschriften, die in London für Salomon angefertigt worden waren, wurden erst kürzlich (1982) von Alec Hyatt King entdeckt; sie sind außerordentlich wichtig.

II. Handschriftliches Orchestermaterial von Johann Elßler

Orchesterstimmen, die nach den autographen Partituren von Haydns eigenem Kopisten geschrieben wurden, viele mit Korrekturen in der Handschrift des Komponisten, sind selbstverständlich von großem Wert bei der Ermittlung eines zuverlässigen Notentextes für die Londoner Sinfonien. Die umfassendste Sammlung ist im Besitz des Fürstenbergischen Archivs in Donaueschingen, wo alle Londoner Sinfonien außer Nr. 100 vorhanden sind. Einige dieser Stimmen sind auf Papier englischer Herkunft geschrieben und offenbar bei den Londoner Aufführungen benutzt worden, bevor Haydn sie mit zurück nach Wien nahm. Das Esterházy-Archiv in Budapest besitzt Stimmen von Elßler zu Nr. 95, 96, 97, 99, 100, 101 und 103 (diese ohne Menuett), und das Archiv Oettingen-Wallerstein in Harburg Nr. 93, 96, 97 und 98.

III. Londoner handschriftliche Partituren

1795 bzw. 1796 übertrug Haydn die Exklusivrechte beider Folgen der Londoner Sinfonien an Salomon – eine noble Geste dem Mann gegenüber, der sie in Auftrag gegeben hatte und unter dessen Leitung als Konzertmeister neun von ihnen uraufgeführt worden waren (die letzten drei Sinfonien wurden im King's Theatre vom neu gegründeten „Opera Concert" unter der Leitung von Giovanni Battista Viotti aufgeführt.) Der „materielle Aspekt" dieses noblen Geschenks bestand aus einem vollständigen Satz Partituren – den Autographen von Nr. 95 und 96 und Kopien der restlichen Werke, wie in Abschnitt I ausgeführt. Im November 1791 schickte Haydn Abschriften der Partituren von Nr. 95 und 96 an seinen Wiener Freund Bernhard von Kees. Offenbar sind sie wohlbehalten angekommen, denn von Kees setzte zu den Anfangstakten beider Werke in seinem Verzeichnis der Sinfonien Haydns den Ver-

merk hinzu: „NB von London gekommen". Die Partituren selbst wurden allerdings bisher nicht aufgefunden.

IV. Gedrucktes Orchestermaterial von Robert Birchall, London

Zweifellos besaß auch Salomon von allen zwölf Sinfonien seinen eigenen Satz Orchesterstimmen. Nach Haydns Rückkehr nach Wien ließ er sie (wozu er nach den Bedingungen der Übereignung berechtigt war) von wenigstens einem Verleger stechen (Monzani & Cimador), und möglicherweise hat er sie außerdem an weitere verkauft. Ein oder zwei Jahre nach Haydns Tod (1809) schloss Salomon eine Vereinbarung mit Robert Birchall (der schon zuvor Salomons Bearbeitungen der Londoner Sinfonien für Klaviertrio sowie für Flöte und Streichquartett und Klavier ad libitum veröffentlicht hatte) über eine Neuausgabe der Orchesterstimmen. Falls Landon mit seiner Annahme recht hat, dass Salomon für diesen Druck Birchall sein eigenes Orchestermaterial zur Verfügung stellte – möglicherweise dasselbe Material, das er bereits unter Haydns Leitung benutzt hatte –, würde dies nicht nur den hohen Standard und den praktischen Charakter der Ausgaben erklären, sondern darüber hinaus auch die oft enge Beziehung zwischen den Stimmen von Birchall und den Autographen und – mit sogar noch größerer Übereinstimmung – zwischen dem Birchall-Druck und den Partitur-Abschriften, die Haydn Salomon geschenkt hatte.

Der Birchall-Druck besitzt also unter den Quellen, auf denen die vorliegende Edition basiert, einen hohen Stellenwert. Mit seiner so engen Beziehung – in der Person Salomons – zu Haydn selbst und mit seiner Tauglichkeit als Aufführungsmaterial verbindet er Vorzüge miteinander, die sowohl für Wissenschaftler wie auch ausübende Musiker von Interesse sind. Wo Birchall von unseren übrigen Quellen abweicht (die Ursache besteht hauptsächlich in Änderungen, die Haydn nach seiner Rückkehr nach Wien vornahm und die Salomon deshalb unbekannt bleiben mussten), werden die Varianten neben anderen wesentlichen

Lesarten in den Einzelanmerkungen unten ausgewiesen.

Editionsprinzipien

Überflüssige Vorsichts- oder wiederholte Akzidentien wurden in einigen Fällen gestrichen. Haydns Gewohnheit, in kontinuierlich modulierenden Passagen den Spielern solche Akzidentien zur Erinnerung fortwährend vorzuschreiben, selbst wenn sie dadurch im selben Takt wiederholt werden, erschwert es, dieses Prinzip konsequent durchzuhalten. In solchen Fällen wurden nur diejenigen Zeichen getilgt, die nach heutigem Gebrauch den Spieler eher verwirren, als dass sie Klarheit schaffen.

Fehlende Akzidentien, Staccato-Zeichen, Artikulations- und Bindebögen, dynamische Bezeichnungen etc. wurden stillschweigend nur dann ergänzt, wenn sie offensichtlich vom Komponisten, Kopisten oder Stecher übersehen wurden. Wenn eine Erläuterung angebracht erscheint, ist sie unten in den Einzelanmerkungen zu finden.

Mit eckigen Klammern und als gestrichelte Bögen sind Herausgeberzusätze im Notentext gekennzeichnet. Die Begründung für solche Ergänzungen (parallele oder analoge Lesarten) ergibt sich aus dem Kontext.

Die Bezeichnung *Tutti*, die Haydn gewöhnlich in den Holzbläserstimmen verwendete, um ein vorausgegangenes Solo aufzuheben, wurde beibehalten, wo es in den benutzten Quellen erscheint. An Stellen, an denen eine Bezeichnung nach dem Kontext eindeutig erforderlich, in den Quellen jedoch nicht ersichtlich ist, wurde das heute übliche [a 2] gesetzt, wenn zwei Stimmen unisono spielen.

Da Haydn und Elßler die Staccato-Vorschrift in aller Regel als flüchtig dahingeworfenen Strich notierten, ist die Entscheidung schwierig, ob Strich und Punkt unterschiedlich ausgeführt werden sollen. Der Herausgeber hat grundsätzlich Punkte gesetzt, es sei denn, ein scharf akzentuiertes staccato schien gefordert.

SINFONIE Nr. 94

Diese Sinfonie wurde zum ersten Mal in den Hanover Square Rooms, London, am 23. März im Rahmen des sechsten Konzerts der 1792 von Salomon gegebenen Konzertreihe unter der Leitung von Haydn als Cembalist und mit Salomon als Konzertmeister aufgeführt. Sie hatte außerordentlichen Erfolg und wurde bald zu einer der bis heute beliebtesten Sinfonien Haydns.

Die englische Bezeichnung „Surprise" bezieht sich auf den *fortissimo* Akkord im II. Satz, Takt 16, eine Passage, die ursprünglich ohne diesen Effekt geschrieben war. Der Name stammt nicht vom Komponisten; ihn gefunden zu haben wurde später vom Londoner Flötisten Andrew Ashe beansprucht, der berichtete, dass „mein geschätzter Freund Haydn mir dafür dankte, dass ich ich [der Sinfonie] einen so angemessenen Namen gab."[5] Bis heute ist die Sinfonie allgemein als „Surprise" oder auf Deutsch als „Sinfonie mit dem Paukenschlag" bekannt.

Quellen

Partiturautograph in der Staatsbibliothek zu Berlin – Preußischer Kulturbesitz, Musikabteilung Berlin und Library of Congress Washington . . . . AUT
Partitur Abschrift nach dem Autograph von Johann Elßler oder einem anderen Kopisten am Hofe Esterházy mit ähnlicher Handschrift im Esterházy Archiv Budapest . . . . BUD
Partitur Abschrift nach dem Autograph, in London für Salomon angefertigt . . . . LON
Handschriftliche Stimmen von Elßler im Fürstenberg Archiv Donaueschingen . . . . D/E
Druckausgabe Birchall . . . . BIR
Zur Überprüfung zweifelhafter Stellen wurde gelegentlich Salomons Quintett- Bearbeitung herangezogen . . . . SAL

Harry Newstone

---

[5] H. C. Robbins Landon, *Haydn – Chronicle and Works* (Bd. 3 *Haydn in England*), London, 1976, S. 149.

Textual Notes

Mov. I

bar 3 Vla. last group, no slur in sources except BIR which slurs nn2–3 (d′–e′)

10 Fg. *p* from BIR, AUT, D/E, BUD have it in middle of 11, LON no dynamic

12 Fl., Ob. ◁ from BIR

15 Str., Cor. stacc. from Vc/Cb. in AUT, LON

16 Vl. I BIR as other sources, all other parts *fp* instead of *fz*

Beginning of exposition BIR has *Vivace* only.

It is important to note the precise position and shape of the sign ◇ in the main theme. It is not only invariably misplaced but misrepresented in all modern editions (including Landon's complete edition, i.e. as

♩ ♪ | ♫♫ ♩ ♪ whereas every one of our sources shows that Haydn clearly wrote ♩ ♪ | ♫♫ ♩ ♪. Not only is it rather a short, closed sign, but its apex is under the quaver, the intention obviously being a kind of accent and not a cresc.-dim. 'hairpin' effect which (as Landon has noted) is impossible to bring off at *Vivace assai*. Later in the movement (bb200, 201, 218, 222) Haydn actually writes ♩ ♪ | ♫♫ ♩ ♪ and SAL consistently shows the figure ♩ ♪ | ♫♫ ♩ ♪ throughout the movement.

19 Vl. I ♫ in AUT, BUD, LON (but not in 41). D/E originally as AUT but changed to ♫, BIR consistently

20 Vl. II nn4–6 slurred in BIR (also 42)

21 Tr. (Clarino in G) crossed out in AUT and *a parte* written above stave. New parts (in C) written out separately for Mov. I and incorporated in all our sources. Vl. II nl low b in BIR (also 158); Fg. 21 as 22 (ditto 158) BIR.

24–30 Vl. I phrasing somewhat inconsistent in MS sources – we follow BIR (also 161–7). (SAL changes Haydn's ♫♫♫ to ♫♫♫)

29 Fl., Ob. semiquaver slur from BIR (also 166)

30 Vl. II originally ♫. Haydn changed it here but forgot to do so at 167. The correction at 167 is made in

LON and appears in BIR, one of many examples demonstrating a closer link between BIR and LON than BIR and AUT.

50 Vl. II n2, lower note d' in LON, D/E, BIR (& SAL)

58 Vl. II nn2–3 slur from BIR

62 Vl. I *fz* (×2) from LON where they appear (*sf*) in another hand (Salomon's ?) and BIR. Fl. tie to 63 possible on basis of Cor., Tr. (partially supported in sources) but BIR has *sf* for Fl. both bars.

63 Str., Ob., Fg. *fz* from BIR (also LON – Salomon's hand ?)

64, 65 Vl. I/II, Fl. *fz* from 181/2 most sources, slurs from Vl. I/II 181/2 LON, BIR

70, 71 Vl. I mostly ♫♫♫♫ in LON, BIR

75 Vl. I, Fl. we show an interesting change made in LON (in Haydn's hand ?) for nn1–6 and engraved so in BIR. All other sources 75 repeats 74 for nn1–6.

79 Vl. II n1–3 slur from BIR 228 (confirmed both times in SAL)

80–90 Str. (and Fl.) phrasing largely from BIR; ditto Str. (and Ob.) 229–39. BIR's very practical phrasing (bowing) for Vl. II in both places is worthy of note and is suggested for Vla., Vc.

93 Fg. d in AUT, BUD, D/E. LON *col basso* at this point, i.e. b – which is what BIR Fg. has and we believe to be the correct reading.

93–95 Ob. 1 *tr* over each bar in AUT, BUD, LON, D/E (LON also 96), our continuous *tr* ～～ from BIR (ditto 242–5)

96, 97 Vl. I (& Fl. 97) phrased ♪ in BIR (partly in LON); ditto 245/6

107, 108 Vl. II, Vla. and 109–10 Vl. II slurs from BIR

115–118 Vl. I, Ob. 1, slurs from BIR; Vl. II BIR has interesting phrasing ♫♫♫♫ ♫♫ | ⸸ |. Our other sources have a mixture of ♫ and ♫, mostly the former (ditto SAL).

126, 128, 130 Cor., Tr., Timp. n1 *p* in BIR. Ditto D/E Tr. but in another hand.

131 Mixture of *f* and *ff* in sources. We standardize *ff* (confirmed in SAL).

131-134 Timp. AUT originally had a (intending a change of tuning or a third drum), changed in another hand to g (131/2) and d (133/4) with *NB* above each alteration. BUD retains the original notation and LON has the alteration written over the original. Similarly BIR has the alteration but was clearly first engraved as the original. D/E has d throughout.

141 Fg. n1 *8ve* lower in BIR

148 Vc/Cb. quavers slurred in BIR

160 Cor. 2 n1 e′ in AUT, BUD, D/E; LON has e′ but c′ written lightly below it, BIR has c′ (see b23)

164 Tr. minim d″ in AUT (part written out separately), BUD, D/E crossed out in LON and ♩♪♪ written in. BIR follows this as we do.

177-179 Str. slurs from LON (Vl. I), BIR (all); also Fg. 178 BIR

180 Tr. 2 LON c″ crossed out and downward stem added to Tr. 1e″ (i.e. Tr. 2 = Tr. 1), this change shown in BIR

182 Cor. *fz* from BIR

187 Vl. I second group ♫♫♫ in AUT, BUD, D/E and LON which also applies this phrasing to both groups in 188

191 Vl. I phrasing of first group from BIR. Editorial phrasing 191/2/3 from Ob. 1 193 (all sources *but* BIR!). (SAL Vl. I 191-3 has ♫♫♫ ♫♫♫.)

199 Timp. *p* in AUT, BUD, D/E. LON also has *p* in Vl. I (another hand) and Cor. BIR applies the *p* (or *pp*) to all the parts (Vl. II, Ob. 2 middle of bar) except Vla. The return to *f* b204 n2 is in LON and BIR.

213-214 Ob. 2 stave empty AUT, BUD, rests D/E. LON has Ob. 2 as Ob. 1 but struck out and the notes we show inserted in another hand. This alteration is in BIR.

224-226 Fg. stacc. from D/E which also has ⎯⎯ 225/6 and ⎯⎯ 227 (possibly a later addition, though SAL Vl. I has *f* middle of b226)

241 Vc/Cb. ♩ ⁊ ♩ ⁊ BIR (& SAL). Other sources have minim – Haydn may have forgotten that Vc/Cb. are pizz. here. 248 arco all sources (except LON).

253 Timp. dotted crochet in all MS sources. Surely mistake – corrected in BIR (i.e. as b251).

Mov. II

The AUT of this movement, together with the last page (six bars) of I, is in the Library of Congress, Washington. The first two eight-bar sections have repeat signs, the vlas. have a harmony part, and there is no 'surprise'. Haydn crossed out these two sections and rewrote them fully with different orchestration for the repeats – adding the famous *ff* chord. No holograph score of this final version has come to light and no parts have been found of the 'original' version. All our sources have Haydn's revision.

bar 9 Vl. I *pp* from D/E; also in Vla. in another hand

16 Tr. stave empty BUD. The loud chord variously marked *f*, *ff* and *fz* in sources. We follow BIR which has *ff* in all parts (but Fl. - *f*).

26 Vl. I/II, Vc/Cb. AUT as b18; all other sources Vla. ♫ ,, Vc/Cb. ♩ ♩.

33 Str., Fl. *ff* in BIR. Vl. II, Vla. *p* on n2 in AUT, LON, BIR; on n3 BUD, *fp* n1 D/E. Cor. 2, Tr. 2 c′ in BIR.

39 Vl. I *fz* middle of bar LON (another hand), engraved in BIR (& SAL). D/E has *fz* beginning of bar followed by *p*.

42 Vl. I AUT tiny slur nn1–2 copied literally in BUD. D/E, BIR add stacc. dots to nn3, 4 (ditto 44). LON (& SAL) extend slur over nn1–4.

44 Vla. slur to 45 added on basis of Vl. II bb20–1 BUD, LON, D/E, BIR and 28–9 LON. D/E, BIR ♫ ♪ ,.

55 Vl. I/II, Vla. semiquaver slur from BIR (only over nn1–2 in Vl. I)

57–60 Vl. I/II second half of each bar only BIR has slurs, but ♫♫ ♫ in Vl. I and ♫♫ ♫ in Vl. II, the same inconsistency in 61–5 and 67

58 Vl. II LON faint alteration to d″; 60 ditto to e♭″

66, 67 Ob. 2 BIR last note in each bar a′ and d″ respectively

69 W/w slur last six notes from BIR

70 Vl. I slur from BIR (& SAL). BIR places *p* at beginning of bar.

72 Vl. I slur nn3–5 from BIR (SAL has ♩ ♫♫)

87, 88 Ob. 1 phrasing from LON, BIR and *fz* BIR; other sources slur over the two bars and no *fz*

96 Fl., Ob. slur nn3–5 from BIR (ditto 104)

107 Vl. I slur nn4–6 AUT, BUD, 10–12 BUD; other sources stacc. 135 same slurs in AUT, BUD, D/E and this time BIR. LON stacc. both times.

109 Timp. note in AUT, BUD, D/E. In LON it has been struck out and minim rest written in and BIR (interestingly) has bar rest.

118 Vla. all sources have ♩♪♪♩ except BIR which has ♪♪ ♩ ^ten. which we feel to be correct

129 Vc/Cb., Fg. have long been misprinted ♪ ♪♪ ♪, but all sources clearly have ♪♪ ♪♪ (except D/E which has the former in Vc/Cb. and the latter in Fg.!)

134 Ob. 1 ♫ ♪ in AUT, BUD, D/E. Our ♫♫ ♪ from LON, BIR. Fg. last four notes slurred in BIR (but not Str.).

135 Vl. II top note in first chord (c″) not in LON, D/E, BIR

136 Fl., Ob. 1 ten. from BIR, added to Ob. 2. Timp. as AUT, LON; other sources have four quavers.

138 Vl. II, Vla. ff in BIR (also in another hand in D/E Vla.)

139–142 Vl. I, Vc/Cb., W/w stacc. dots inconsistently distributed in sources but BIR has them in most parts

142 Vl. I lower note at fermata (c″) from LON, BIR (and SAL); Timp. roll sign (•••••) from AUT, LON, BUD (D/E, BIR just ♪ ⌢).

145 The pp under the Vla. part is probably meant to serve for all Str. BIR Cor. 1 and pp here and at 149 (Ob., Fg. soli and Vc/Cb.) and 153 (Ob. 2, Cor., Vl. I/II)

Mov. III

The first two pages of AUT (28 bars) are missing

bar 1 The f at the beginning is from BIR. The two quavers (upbeat to bb1, 5, 9, 41, 45) are slurred in one or other of the parts in LON and BIR

13, 15 Vl. I LON, BUD, BIR have tr, D/E + (SAL nothing)

16 Vc/Cb. nn1–2 slurred in LON, BIR; BIR applies it also to Vla., Fg.

17 Vla. slur from LON, BIR

30 Vl. II bottom note b♭ and 31 middle note g′ in BIR

35-37 Tr. originally $\flat$ —┤♭ —┤♭. in LON (as AUT, BUD, D/E) but changed (another hand) to ♩ ♪ ♪ |♩ ♪ ♪ |♩ ♪ ♪. This alteration also in BIR.

38 Fl. *Solo* from BIR (no dynamic), D/E has *p* in another hand. Ob. *p* from BIR.

47 Vl. I middle note in chord (d″) as AUT, BUD, LON; D/E, BIR have c″ (as 45, 46)

53 Ob. 1, Cor. 1 slurs from BIR; Ob. 2 stacc. in AUT, BUD; Ob. 1/2 stacc. in LON, (Vl. II stacc. in SAL)

55-58 Fg. 𝄢 ⬩⬩⬩⬩ in BIR; LON as BIR 55 only, then as other sources

56 Vl. I has small puzzling *f* in AUT (& BUD), shown as *fz* in LON. Could apply to Fl. Not in D/E or BIR.

55-61 Vl. I/II, Vla., Fl., Ob. 1 editorial slurs from BIR and SAL (legato clearly intended though inconsistently shown – i.e. BIR Fl. engraved ♪♩ ♩♩)

68-69 Vl. II, Vla. editorial slur on basis of Vl. II 87-8 BIR

72-75 Vl. II no phrasing in any of our main sources; perhaps ♫♫♫ from Vl. I meant to continue. SAL has

♫♫♫ which is applied also to 76, 78 (Vla. ditto).

Mov. IV

bar 3, 4 Vl. II slur possibly meant to reach f♯ or even g. In b12 AUT slur is under the three quavers and not from 11, and at 106-7 it seems to extend over both bars.

5 Vl. II n2 slur to b6 n1 in BIR which has this phrasing across the bar line in a number of other places – i.e. Vl. I 9-10 (though not Fl.), Vc/Cb. 11-12, Vla. 17-20 (though not Vl. II)

18, 20 Vl. I AUT originally had something other than the semi-quavers, with slur from the previous bars (see comments to b5 above). This slur is retained in most sources and BIR adds one to the semiquavers in 191 (Fl.) and 193 (Vl. I) which reading we adopt here too.

24 Vl. II, Vla. slur to 25 from BIR

27, 28 Vla., Vc/Cb. slurs from BIR

34 Vl. I ornament not clear in AUT, could be ✛ or *tr*, all our sources have *tr*, including SAL which adds it logically to Fl.

44–46 Ob.2, Fg., Vla., Vc/Cb. semiquaver slurs from BIR; ditto 58, 60 Obs., Fg., Vl. II, Vla., Vc/Cb.

44–62 Fg. LON bass clef and empty stave (i.e. *col basso*) not noticing that Fg. and Vc/Cb. are not the same in 48–51. The mistake is carried over to BIR (further evidence that BIR is based on LON rather than on AUT).

55 Ob. 1 AUT short slur nn2–3, BUD, D/E over all four notes, LON slur nn2–4. Our phrasing from BIR (& Fl.).

63 Vl. I nn2–3 slurred D/E, other sources slur nn1–2 (& Fl.); AUT hasty slur in Vl. can be read either way, or even over whole bar

101 Vl. I semiquaver slur BIR only

113 Vl. I last note d''' in D/E (see also 255)

121 Vl. II last note slur to 122 from BIR, ditto 123–4. Applied to 163–4 and 165–6.

121, 123 Vla., Vc/Cb. slur nn2–3 from BIR, also at 163, 165 where LON has it

122 Vl. I BIR n5 (b'') has cautionary ♮ which was first engraved ♭

154–155 Vl. I, Vla. slur across barline BIR

160 Fl., Ob. 1 n1 slurred from 159 in BIR (as previous bars); BUD Ob. 1/2 stacc. and BIR Ob. 2 stacc.

162 Vla. nn1–2 [music notation] in LON (another hand, the stave being empty - *col basso* as in AUT). The alteration is also in BIR.

163ff. W/w slurs on basis of 121ff., confirmed in Ob. 2 BIR (163–9)

167 Ob. 2 n1 changed (another hand) to a' in LON, perhaps to retain the shape of the previous bars. Alteration in BIR.
Fg. n2 [music notation] in BIR.

168 Vl. II nn2–3 slurred AUT, LON. D/E slurs all six semiquavers in pairs, BIR slurs in pairs to middle of b171. We apply this to Vla.

180 Vl. I phrasing only in AUT, LON - obviously applies also to 181

206 Fg. 2 low d AUT only but not perfectly placed and could be a small blot; all other sources Fg. 2 as Fg. 1

208 Fg. n2 an *8ve* lower in BIR; Timp. rests

222 Vl. I *f* on n2 in BIR (& SAL)

225 Fl., Ob. *p* and Fg. *dol.* (no dynamic) from BIR

226 Timp. *pp* in BIR

227 Vl. I/II (pizz.) *p* from BIR, other sources no dynamic (except SAL where the pizz. is on Vl. II only and marked *f*)

229 Ob. 2 n1 usually printed g′; all our sources have b′

233 Timp. no *f* in BIR until 234

234 Timp. *f* crossed through in LON and replaced by crotchet and crotchet rest (another hand). The crochet in 235 appears also to have been crossed through in LON, perhaps to avoid the momentary clash with the a♭ in Vc/Cb., Fg. BIR reflects the LON changes in 234–5.

235 Vl. II upper note f′ from LON, BIR (& SAL). AUT, BUD, D/E have a♭′ but we think the change sensible

255 Vl. I/II last note e‴ in LON, BIR (& SAL)

264 Fg. *8ve* higher in BIR; ditto D/E after correction from e

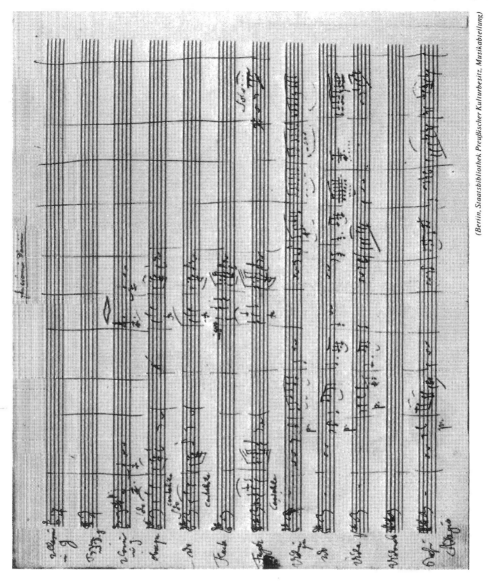

(Berlin, Staatsbibliothek Preußischer Kulturbesitz, Musikabteilung)

First page from the autograph score
Erste Seite aus dem Autograph der Partitur

SYMPHONY No. 94
'Surprise'

In Nomine Domini

Joseph Haydn
(1732–1809)

Edited by Harry Newstone
© 2009 Ernst Eulenburg Ltd, London
and Ernst Eulenburg & Co GmbH, Mainz

3

4

II. Andante

III. Menuetto

Allegro molto

Trio

Menuetto da capo

IV. Finale

Allegro di molto

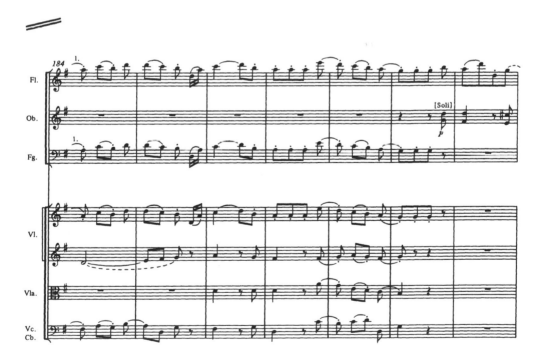

Finis Laus Deo